GRONW'S STONE

Voices from the Mabinogion

New Year 97

To Auntie Beryl
with love

Edmund

GRONW'S STONE

Voices from the Mabinogion

ANN GRAY

EDMUND CUSICK

HEADLAND

First published in 1997
by
HEADLAND PUBLICATIONS
North Wales & Wirral

Tŷ Coch, Galltegfa, Llanfwrog,
Ruthin, Clwyd. LL15 2AR
and
38 York Avenue, West Kirby,
Wirral, Merseyside. L48 3JF

British Library Cataloguing in Publication Data.
A full CIP record for this book is available from the British Library.

ISBN: 0 903074 97 4

Printed in Great Britain by
L. Cocker & Co., Berry Street, Liverpool.

With grateful thanks to Tŷ Newydd
for the week when we first saw Gronw's Stone.

ACKNOWLEDGEMENTS

'Pwyll' was awarded third prize in the Aberystwyth Open Poetry Competition in 1995. 'Pwyll' and 'Gwydion' were selected for the *Aberystwyth Open Poetry Competition Anthology* for 1995. 'Gwydion to Lleu' appeared in *Avalon* Magazine, Spring 1996.

Cover illustration, and illustrations throughout, by Margaret Jones.

CONTENTS

INTRODUCTION

These poems arise from an exploration of the power and the province of *The Mabinogion;* and specifically from a week spent at Tŷ Newydd with Hugh Lupton and Eric Maddern, where the stories came alive in the hill forts, the mountains, the lakes, the castles and finally, beside a smoky wood fire in a roundhouse in the middle of the night. For both of us, *The Mabinogion* will always live in these memories, although we have tried to read every translation, every collection of stories and poems since.

It is this magic that we want to share.

Our intention is not to retell the Four Branches of *The Mabinogion*. These poems give voices to the men and women, whether they be Kings or Queens, daughters of Giants, Wizards or Lap-Maidens, from this world or the other. We hope to provoke new encounters for readers already familiar with the stories. For those of you who are meeting them for the first time we have provided brief outlines of the relevant passages of the four branches to set the poems in context. We hope, however, that you will be inspired to read *The Mabinogion* or, better still, find a way to hear it told, for it is in its oral tradition that it is most alive.

Ann Gray and Edmund Cusick

THE FIRST BRANCH

THE FIRST BRANCH

Pwyll, Prince of Dyfed, hunted in the forests of Arberth. At the end of the day his hounds picked up the scent of a great stag, and brought it to bay in the woods of Glyn Cuch. As Pwyll approached he saw another pack around the stag, each hound of which was pure white. No sooner had he driven them off than Arawn, King of Annwn, the otherworld, appeared, whose hounds they were. To amend the dishonour he had done to the King, Pwyll agreed to do anything he should ask of him. The King requested that Pwyll change places with him for a year and a day. At the end of that year Pwyll should fight a duel with Hafgan, whose lands in Annwn bordered Arawn's.

During his year in Annwn, all that the King had, his hall, his men, his hounds and his horses, would belong to Pwyll, even his wife. The enchantment was such that none was aware of the deception. Pwyll ruled Annwn well, but although he could conduct himself tenderly by day, he found his honour forbade him to touch the Queen at night. When the year ended Pwyll fought and killed Hafgan, and returned to Dyfed.

One day he rode to the enchanted hill of Gorsedd Arberth. Here, it was said, if any dared to stand upon it he would either see a great marvel or suffer grievous blows. It was here he first caught sight of Rhiannon, riding on a white horse, whom he later married. After they had been married for several years Rhiannon gave birth to a son. Six serving women were ordered to keep watch over mother and child, but failed to do so. During the night the child vanished. Fearful of punishment, the women pretended Rhiannon herself had destroyed her child in a fit of madness after childbirth. They killed newborn puppies from her hounds, smeared Rhiannon's face and hands with blood, and scattered bones among the bedclothes. Rhiannon was found guilty. Her punishment was to wait for seven years outside the gates, telling strangers her story and offering to carry them on her back into the city. After several years a series of magical events, and the loyalty of Teyrnon and his wife, restored her child, Pryderi, to her.

THE QUEEN OF ANNWN

My Lord, at first I thought
it was something I had said
that had offended.
For days I listened to my voice
to try to catch my words
in some discourtesy.
Then I imagined it was
something about my person
you found distasteful. Each day
I bathed and had my maids
dip loosestrife in the water,
skim mullein through my hair,
and still you turned your back to me,
night after endless night until
I learned to dread the fall of light,
the time you might, once more,
refuse me. If you had but laid
one finger on my back, I would
have wept with pleasure.
I cannot live this lie by day,
turn my body to your smile
as if the dark hours never happen.
I have used Homerical charms,
woven binding and loosing spells,
strung nine spancels of horse-hair
in the canopies of our bed.
In my erotic melancholy
I have gathered jimson weed,
sweat from mares in heat, snatched
scarlet rowan berries from
the standing stones. I have stumbled
up cliffs in the snow blind moon
to find mothan for your philtres,
and still you leave me burning.
I have stolen honey from the comb,
covered all the soft parts
of my body, rolled in grass,

picked off the grains and ground them,
baked the bread for you to eat -
but you are hexed, or taken
from me. I have played the pipes,
talked to the water wagtail,
taken thorn apples in my skirts,
dried the summer roots of orchis.
Last moon I used all kinds of stone,
all strength of herbs, my menstrual blood.
I would have ground my navel string,
powdered it in your wine, had I
but kept it. Raging and witless,
I search for creeping things, new fruits,
windflowers, wintergreen, comfrey.

It is now one whole year since
this began, and I am broken.
Is it your wish, my Lord, that I
take leave of all my senses.

PWYLL

Nothing may I take from you
whom I have lain by for a year,
not even your leave.
Behind my eyelids I see ivory hounds
gleaming around the stag I brought to bay,
my own dogs shivering.
That night I first came to you,
dressed in your husband's flesh,
your skin was blue-white as his hounds, your body
wet as snow for me, your touch eager, burning
like ice that steals the blood heat from the mouth.
Something held me back, though you were willing,
that night, and each night since. It was not fear,
nor yet honour for he whose place I took.
I wished, perhaps, to keep some deed untrespassed;
desiring, but not wanting, this last communion;
knowing I would care for no mortal woman
after you. And it is so.
You do not know me, trapped
behind your master's eyes,
guess only disdain as I turn my face to the wall.
Each night, I hear desire
and pride wrestle in your breathing;
after that, despair.
The sun's warmth strokes your hair,
embraces you. Before night falls
I will hunger for you,
wish I had been
less pure.

RHIANNON AT THE GATES

Good Day to you. If it is.
I know not. Blood. Blood
in the sunrise, in the bed.
If you wish, I could carry you
on my back into the city.
If you do not, it matters little.
I sit here, watching days,
counting years. Six years old
if he were here and I have
never named him; yet his name
tears my guts, knots my chest,
and shames me. My son.
Blood. Send me the night,
brown blankets of rain, the shuffling
hounds. With them, I crouch
howling at the moon.
Blood on the moon.
I thread it through my fingers,
paint it thick upon my thighs,
to remember, to hope such magic
might return him. Those nights
my breasts gather tight with milk,
weep sweet, white across my belly.
I have suckled my master's hounds,
lain down beside their food, hoped
they would tear me limb from limb
whilst they were eating. My son.
One more year. I have gained
nothing. No part of my pain
has been lifted. Blood
underneath my nails,
between my toes.
You do not wish to talk?
It matters little. My son.
Blood.

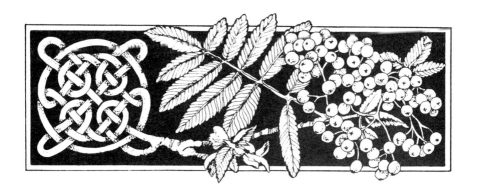

THE SECOND BRANCH

THE SECOND BRANCH

Branwen, daughter of the Welsh King, Bran, was married to the King of Ireland in a bid to unite the two countries. When he heard of this, her half-brother Efnysien savagely maimed the Irish King's horses. Later, at the Irish court, the memory of this was revived, and Branwen, who had given birth to a son, Gwern, was punished. She was imprisoned in the kitchens and brutalised daily. Eventually her father came to her rescue, and raised war to avenge the insults that had been paid to her. In the chaos that followed she was forced to watch her own son being burned to death by Efnysien. Bran himself was wounded in the foot by a poisoned spear. Before the poison could work through his body, he commanded that his own head be struck off, so that he could continue to speak to his companions after his death. With Bran's severed head the seven warriors who alone had survived the conflict returned at last to Harlech. There Branwen died, and there they began a feast. It is said that whilst they ate, the birds of Rhiannon, who can charm the living and wake the dead, came to them. Seven years passed.

EFNYSIEN

I am too late. She is
already sold
for him to make
his child in

white blades of moonlight
pierce the stable's
planks, slice
my quick breath
clouding in the air

as all others sleep, he enjoys
her, parts her lips with wine,
with one wet finger soothes
shut her eyes, strokes
her long lashes.
His hot tongue explores
the secret passage of her ear;
finds the red rash where
the damp mane of her hair
falls on her nape, the mole
beneath her arm, the rough skin
around her thighs

in this chill dark the stink
of dung and hay, the pungent smell
of the mare's heat, the reek
of oatmeal soaked with mead
still wet about their mouths.
Their breath rasps heavy, lifting
the distended womb
which holds the huge headed
foal. Beneath the lids
their eyes twitch pale. Bridle
and harness knotted tight
to bind till it is done

his hand inside her gown, he feels
the sweet swell of her heavy breasts
breathes in the musk of her damp loins

a flood of hot blood, mucus, spurting
on knife and arm, the grate
of blade on bone.
And after, the grooms aroused
from sweating slumber, naked
in the skinned eye of the moon,
whinnying their girlish
terror, the straw stained dark,
the bridal honoured

BRANWEN

Seven of you will return. I can go
no further. Later you can say
I looked back across the sea
and my heart broke. Two good
islands laid waste because of me.
You can say anything you want.
I ceased to live when I was thrown
into the kitchens, when the butcher's
hands, rank with blood, bruised
my face. His foetid breath will
always be just one whisper away.
At night, I strained to hear the smallest
sounds a child might make whilst he
was sleeping. I stretched my arms
into his cot to smooth him, to croon
soft songs, to say, mother hears you;
woke cramped and weeping on the floor.
In all those years I reared nothing
but a starling, taught him the stories
of my childhood. His message
brought you, brought me the double
curse of Efnysien, whose name I spit
across the water. I do not care
for his heroic deeds, his late amends.
Wherever he hopes to rest, I will
torment him. Bury me here. Dig me
a four sided grave so I may look out
on all four corners of the earth.
Wherever you are, I will be watching.
You will remember how I was wronged.

BRAN

Mars burns in the archer's grasp,
Orion stumbles to the earth. Death
is in me. Her kiss scalds my veins,
scours clean the heart of lies.

the spider spins her spiral dance
one strand is will, and one is chance

Venom threads my veins. Now I sense
the poison all around me,
seeping in sap and leaf.
In the serpent's womb a clutch of eggs
death curled in every shell,
and in each tiny skull the elixir
that opens paradise. While
I grew to manhood, took my crown,
so was planted in the womb
the one whose task it was
to slay me: all are bound
by a single thread.

the spider spins her jagged wheel
one strand to maim, and one to heal

The flesh submits, dying into pain,
the spirit wrestles to be free, twisting
through curtained lights, shadows.
Into that violet darkness spirits
press, tempting the reluctant soul, opening
avenues of emerald light. Now come
scents of figs, apricots
and honey, voices of those
as yet unborn, and of my daughter, greeting.

the spider spins her jagged wheel,
one strand to maim, and one to heal

Death's labour is as my birth. The warm dark
of the flesh opens into light and pain.
Now I see the fate that I have lived
unknowing, the soul's spell
that bound me from my birth. On earth
the midwife bites the cord
lets fall the string of flesh,
and on the hill of apples,
three women, weaving, add
a silver strand to their bright loom.

the spider spins her spiral dance
one strand is will, the other chance

The web is cast around us in the dark
and in each act and choice we grasp
at unseen cords, pull the noose tighter,
twisting to be free.

Strike off my head.

MANAWYDAN

I remember only a castle
high by the sea, snow driving,
hissing in the grate. Then stones
baking in the summer heat, the swift
flicker of the leaves' turning
as we passed the flagon. They say
we told tales for seven years. There were
tales we did not tell: the stink
of the heaped dead, the din
of crows, the cold couplings
of the slain, the song a baby sings,
burning. Branwen's white hand
we could not cover, pointing
stiff through the thin soil, the grate
of a blunted sword in bone.

PRYDERI : THE BIRDS OF RHIANNON

Between two lands, in the company
of the dead we journeyed, fleeing
the sun's red gleam,
and ever by the ship, three birds, borne
between cloud and wave, lamenting.

Then coming in that hall the creatures
of Rhiannon, winged like birds,
eyes cold as gulls', watchful
as the heron's, their hooked
nails shining in the firelight,
their voices harsh and clear
as the swan's dying. One had
Branwen's eyes, lamented with her voice
as yet unused to death, sweet
nightmare of the soul's surviving
who sowed her songs among us
and with them a breath
of peace, a glimmer in the soul
a hint of rest, of ending.

THE THIRD BRANCH

THE THIRD BRANCH.

After many adventures, Pryderi and Manawydan returned to Wales, where Manawydan married Rhiannon, Pwyll's widow and Pryderi's mother. Together Pryderi, his wife Cigfa, Manawydan and Rhiannon rode to the hill of Gorsedd Arberth. On the hill top, a violent storm broke, and when the darkness cleared, they found themselves in a country full of a marvellous light, but empty of people. While hunting in this country the dogs of Pryderi and Manawydan flushed out a white boar. Pryderi followed it, and found himself in a Caer, or castle, where there had been none before. He entered it, but did not return. When Manawydan reported news of his loss to Rhiannon, Rhiannon followed Pryderi into the Caer. Neither returned, and, with a peal of thunder, the Caer disappeared. Cigfa was left alone with Manawydan. After many adventures, Manawydan succeeded in restoring Rhiannon and Pryderi from the enchantment which had been placed upon them.

PRYDERI

It faces me, at last, my fear
made flesh. My destiny, a boar
with white flanks streaked
with mud and dung.
Now in an instant I see my life,
its thread twisted from others
tales, passed from tongue
to tongue: Prince Pwyll returned
from Annwn, Rhiannon redeemed
from guilt, the child from unknown
horrors. *Each night the candle burns*
by his bed, the unsheathed knife
lies chill beneath his pillow
lest it return. Wherever he sleeps,
his cries, whimpering,
sound from the room.
My first mother the demon
whose tender claws took me
to the dark. Its wan creatures
have followed me from dream to dream
down the long nightmare
of my nights: the gleaming hounds
my father faced, the pale horse
my mother rode, the breasts of Annwn's
Queen. I have spent my fear
in whiteness. And waking,
I have hunted all creatures
of that hue, the hare
and winter stoat, brought fair
skinned women to lay on fur
and ermine, found that there is none
so white she will not bleed.

It turns, smells my fear.
I follow.

RHIANNON

I should not have raised my voice
to Manawydan. He is a good man.

My son, my blood.
I thought my care was ended.

Manawydan knows. He sees me
pace the corners of my room,
shake the pillows, fold the quilts,
turn back the linen. He tries
to soothe me into sleep, the nights
I dare not close my eyes for fear
I find myself again at the gates,
stooped, the smell of blood before me.

I wear blue stones silvered
in my bracelets, turn them over
in my anxious hands, whisper
keep safe, three times, five times,
nine times. At Sirius' rising
I gather vervain, bruise the leaves
distil them. I have purselain,
cinquefoil, star of the earth,
bloodroot, broomtops boiled
with wine, and still I cut the rowan
and wear it on my saddle.

My son, my blood.
I thought my care was ended.

It is as they said. This is the place.
The air is chill, enchanted.
Shadows chase between the trees.
No birds sing. No birds.
The air is tight with silence,
no noise of dogs in answer to
my stepping horse, no voices,
yet somewhere deep inside,
the soft splash of falling water.

My son, my blood.
I thought my care was ended.

CIGFA

This is a desolate place
sudden mists suffocate
the sun no sound of dogs
still   even in the trees
no breath   no birdsong
shadows purple the oaks
chestnuts   slate against
the sky   mud pulls
thirstily at my skirts
matted tassels of my shawl

Pryderi will not return
nor Rhiannon

It would be as good
to die as to live
no falling of the moon
sun rising

Rhiannon   mother
sister   your hands
in my hair
at my waist
your laugh which never
reached your eyes
your son   my husband

chill   I would move
I have no words
to break this waiting
to summon shapes
shifting through the trees
no boiling broth
no plants   stones

it would be as good
to die as to live
to close my eyes
to see golden
to dream the far off sound
of falling water

PRYDERI AT THE CAER

In magic was I born and will I die.
At Gorsedd Arberth I saw my fate
revealed. There was no death there,
in that other country
that dawned through the mist.
That world we found,
the image of our own, shot through
with light; the stones glittering: jade, serpentine,
emerald. It lies there always,
perhaps, within our hills, our souls'
sight too gross to glimpse it. At
its heart, I found a Caer
traced in brittle ice, its gates
frozen into pearl, an altar in
a pool of radiance, a scarlet
chalice. When I touched it, flame
sprang in four swift tongues
piercing my palms, streaming
into heaven, till I cried out, my heart burning
to its metre. And I beheld Gorsedd
Arberth and Golgotha, Caer Sidi
and Jerusalem, Eden and Annwn
bound through this place,
as in the frost the web
binds branch to branch: the stone
raised at Felinrhyd, the stars'
cold dance above Maen Tyryawg.

THE FOURTH BRANCH

THE FOURTH BRANCH

When Math, King of Gwynedd, was not at war, he rested his feet in the lap of a maiden. Her name was Goewin. Math had two nephews: Gwydion and Gilfaethwy. Gilfaethwy conceived a violent passion for Goewin. As Math was a magician, and could hear every word whispered on the wind, Gilfaethwy told no one. Gwydion his brother was a sorceror, and resolved to help him. By cheating Pryderi, Gwydion started a war with the Kingdom of Dyfed. Math left his court and Goewin unprotected. Together Gwydion and Gilfaethwy raped Goewin, then joined the war in which, with the aid of magic, Gwydion killed Pryderi at Felinrhyd. He was buried at Maen Tyryawg.

When Math returned from war, Goewin told him what had been done to her. Math married her and punished his nephews, transforming them first into a hind and a stag; then a boar and a sow; then a wolf and a she wolf. Each transformation lasted for a year, and in each they produced offspring together: a fawn, a young boar, and a wolf-cub. Then, forgiven, the two brothers were returned to human form.

In search of another lap maiden, Math turned to Gwydion for advice. He suggested Arianrhod, his sister. To test her virginity, Arianrhod had to step over a golden wand, but as she did so, two infants fell from her womb. The first ran to the sea and never returned. The second was seen only by Gwydion, who wrapped it in silk and concealed it in a chest in his room. This child grew to be Lleu, whom Gwydion loved as his own son. Arianrhod, furious with Gwydion, cursed the child that he would have no wife born of mortal woman.

To evade the curse and find Lleu a wife, Math and Gwydion resorted to magic, and conjured a bride from trees and herbs. They named her Blodeuwedd. The tale of the creation of a beautiful woman by the dark arts was retold so often that Blodeuwedd's fame spread far beyond Gwynedd. Alone at court, her husband away hunting, Blodeuwedd heard hunters nearby and instructed her men to offer them hospitality overnight. She met Gronw Pebyr, Lord Of Penllyn, and they became lovers. Despite his anxiety lest Lleu should return, Gronw Pebyr stayed with her for three nights. Blodeuwedd, now determined to kill her husband so that she might be with Gronw, won from Lleu the secret of the charm set on his life. He could only be slain by a spear whose head was forged while all others were at mass. Gronw made the spear and killed Lleu, but his spirit stayed on earth in the form of an eagle, to be restored to human form by Gwydion. Gwydion then punished Blodeuwedd by transforming her into an owl. Gronw, challenged by Lleu, agreed to stand in the place where Lleu had himself received Gronw's spear-cast, to receive one blow from him. Before the blow could be struck, Gronw hid behind a huge slab of rock. Lleu's spear pierced the rock and killed him.

A stone as tall as a man, with a hole over the heart, lies by the river Cynfael to this day.

GWYDION

This caul they saved, my twin,
the sorcerous skin
that once we wore, a thing
enchanted. I like to touch it.

I know your thought,
as I have known your every
wish, since the first time
we lay locked together
in that swollen belly.
You have forgotten this, but I remember
the torn loins,
the blood smeared
across wet sheets, our hungry
biting at the nurse's teats.
Still hot from the dead womb
we clung each to the other.

Three gifts I will give to Pryderi,
each conjured out of darkness:
a shield that will not last
the night, hounds to scent
fresh blood, stallions
to mount his staggering mare.
And I will give you
this woman you desire, conjuring
by other means your chosen
pleasures - these too
I know. Trust me.
This is magic.

And when your little lust
is done, I must follow, push
my cold member into that place
wet with your warm seed,
hard with a different lust.

The spell will follow us,
little brother, I see it.
Our curse then, as our sin, to enact
my own desire. So, made male
and female, boar and sow
I will couple with you
till at last you grow
heavy with me, endure
the agony of birth.

GOEWIN

It was dark when we heard them,
almost the middle of the night.
All the women ran to the windows.
In truth, we thought it might be you
returned from war. Too soon, we knew,
but none could stop us hoping.
Two horsemen, both young, clattered
through your gates, leapt the stairs
two at a time until they reached me,
threw my women to the floor. I ran
until there was no place to run to.
Your nephew, Gilfaethwy, held his hand
across my mouth, tore my clothes
from my body, yet I was frightened
more by his brother. He stood naked,
his member in his hand, waiting;
took me with a desperate lust,
but spent himself across his brother.
Even now, at that time of the night,
his face still swims before me, mirrored,
doubled, twinned; wakes me screaming.
Punish them in some dark way.
Take this nightmare from me.

ARIANRHOD

So, I lied. So did you, my brother,
Gwydion. Let us not forget
that child was yours. What trick was it
to propose me as Math's Lap-Maiden ?
You knew his magic would defeat me.
The last three years had seen you
hind, wild boar and she-wolf. Three
unnatural couplings. Three times
he touched you with his wand, yet
you stood and watched his golden test
of my virginity, knowing
I could not pass it. You shamed me.
How dare you now appear at Caer
Arianrhod and tell me
there is another, a second child.
When you destroyed my reputation
he lost his chance to have a name.
I will not do it. In your honour,
I will curse him threefold. No name.
He will not bear arms unless I choose
which will be never, and as
a testament to the lusts of his father,
no mortal woman will be his wife.
I promise you, whatever powers
you may use to defeat me
will bring him endless pain.

MATH

The air burns. Charcoal spits,
hisses in the censer. The moon
is set. Around this tower
spirits gather, scenting sorcery
as the hound smells blood.
Somewhere an owl screams.
Poised in the turquoise west
Hesperus hangs like pearl.

With a hazel staff I seal this circle.

Saturn, ill aspected, sinks
in the south. Now Lucifer rises
on flickering wings of light
the art begins.

Into the crucible I pour
stinging oil of broom
petals pressed, thrice distilled,
the green sap of an oak
bled in the wet dawn, and this,
still fresh with life:
Ulmaria, Queen
of the meadow, Venus' flower,
Erwain, Bridewort
Meadowsweet.

Along the purple stalk,
a faint white fur. From its
sliced stem I squeeze
one milky drop. A bitter
odour stains the air.

Life stirs in the crucible,
like calls to like. The Goddess
extends her radiance.

Come, Dryad.
By Venus
who rules all your kind,
I conjure you,
Obey!

GWYDION TO LLEU

Behold, my child, your bride,
naked. We have made her
perfect, as none else will be
till women cease begetting,
the belly unscarred by birth, blank
as the smooth stones
of the river. She will not bleed
nor weep at the fickle moon.
Touch her - we have not taught her
shame - her loins tight, moist
as the clefts of wet ferns
by the lilied pools, lips
sweet as strawberries
for you to suck on, breasts
pale as apple's flesh
fresh skinned,
dark at the core.

— So with my brother I have made
three beasts, with my sister, you.
Now to spite a mother's curse
this childless, motherless thing —

The face is comely, too, as you
desired, though the eyes
seem sullen. And she has
a pleasing scent, sharp,
sweet, as summer flowers
crushed in the hand.

BLODEUWEDD TO GRONW

Whatever stories you have heard,
forget them. Touch me.
If you cannot trust your hands,
try your tongue. Did you
dream your hounds would fetch you
such a prize when you set off
this morning, your horses fresh ?
As the day drew on, did you begin
to sense me ? Was it honeysuckle
in my woods that pulled you closer ?
When my men rode out,
were you waiting ?
I have walked through your nights
forever but, until now, you have never
held me. You know the colour
of my hair, the way I turn
my head, part my legs. You smile.
I know you have undressed me.
We are alone here but for
the flickering of the candles.
The only noise, beeswax dripping
on the slate, the sometime shriek
of owls, the whisper of my name
as you take me. Tell me, did it
always feel like this, or is this better ?

LLEU

Dusk falls. I should return
to you. The breath from the low marsh,
of mist and meadowsweet stays me.

You were my wish. To break
my curse, and end six years
of unwanted purity, nights
tainted with the bitter stench
my own longing, solitude.

Give me a woman who is beautiful
who will never refuse me.

On the longest day they brought you
to me. In the fields, Adam's eye, bridewort,
cornflower, poppies, weeping
with dew. The month of broom.

The packed church a crush of bodies
the air thick with herbs
smouldering on the charcoal. Through
the hiss of incense I saw your eyes
liquid, cool, the hues
of violet, larkspur, your body
burning through the thin robe. My wish
incarnate. On the altar cloth
I saw grapes twist and swell, felt
your hand's heat, my ring
too loose on you, but yet
you smiled.

In our chamber, the drink of nutmeg,
mandrake. The bridebed, strewn
with lignum crucis. Beeswax candles
ate the air with honeyed smoke. Your
white limbs parted to receive me.
I sucked nectar from your fingers.
For the first time I tasted knowledge
pungent as musk, my curse
broken. And when you rose
I saw your bare back scarred
with mistletoe, its leaves
etched on you
like wounds, its veins branded
in your blood. After, you ate
berries, drank, fat beads of cream
glistening on your swollen lips,
kissed me till my tongue found
the warm pulp in your mouth.

And in the night, after my strength
was spent, and spent again,
the soft sibilance of your fragrant
breath, pleading, *more.*

It grows late.

Each morning I rise earlier, call
to pale horses, exhausted grooms,
dogs weary of the endless chase.

My Lord, again will you not stay?

But I dream now of my death,
poisoned by strange fruit, drowning
in river weed, strangled by ivy, wake to find
your hair across my face.

Owls call. I must return.

BLODEUWEDD TO GRONW

'I do not advise you to leave me today'

Before I knew you, the dawn broke,
the day began, I walked, I rode,
I dressed for dinner. I never thought
that I could shape my days around
the smallest things, the faintest taste
of lemon on your skin, your short, pale
lashes, the way you tremble, catch
your breath before you take me.
Gronw Pebyr - I adore you -
Feel my power centered in my belly.
I, Blodeuwedd, woman, am huge
with this, drenched, scarlet,
swollen. If I should wish, I know
that I could fly clear of these walls,
above these woods, watch you
always, even in the darkest night.
You will sense me, feel the ghost
draught skating through the leaves,
my breath cold behind your neck,
across your cheek. You will stretch
to touch me. There is no magic
can prevent it. I own my own.
Test me; see if you can leave today,
My Lord of Penllyn.

GRONW

The forge grows hot, demanding
me again. The last sabbath
of a year of sabbaths.
I did not seek
this fate, nor did I
deny it. Blame the stars,
Gronw, or the beast
that led you to her gate.
Its blood not washed
from off me, before she gave
the kiss of greeting. Her dogs,
mine, coupling outside the walls.
And within, Lleu's hall,
strewn with mint and vervain.
Blodeuwedd. You gave me honeycomb
from your hives, broke it
with white fingers, pressed
sweetness to my lips, while
the trembling harpist sang
of another hunt, another Lord's
wife. Your eyes devoured me
as if there were no shame
nor ever had been in that hall.
When I rose
your small fists drew my mouth
to yours, as a child, mad of thirst,
pulls brambles to it
careless of the thorns, brought me
to your bed. And as I entered
you I closed my eyes, drowning
in the breath of honeysuckle
piled by that tall bed
and after, opened them, saw
the slow bees within, clad
in cloying pollen, wings gummed
with nectar, fumbling
in torpor, and I slept.

The iron glows. While you
and he eat Christ's
flesh I labour here. I see
your eyes watching; flickering
in the reeds, the leaves,
impatient. A final stroke.
Here is the spear
to pierce his side.

GRONW'S STONE

For Eric. River Cynfael, October 1994

Then he lifted it,
a huge stone with a hole in it,
and held it over his heart.
It was here, he said,
that Gronw was killed.
We lifted our eyes to the mountains,
watched the magic streaming
sunlight, shafting through the trees.

THE POETS

Of **Ann Gray** in her first collection, *Painting Skin* (Fatchance Press, 1995), Sylvia Kantaris said: 'Unnerving in her intimate confrontations with love and loss'. Penny Windsor commented in *Tears in the Fence*: 'Ann Gray is mistress of the short poem which catches a moment, a mood, and holds it on the page delicately, as though, without print, it would vanish.' Ann Gray is currently editing an anthology of food poems, *Having Your Cake and Eating It*. She is widely published. Her poems have been broadcast on radio, danced to and set to music. She apppeared in the 1995 *Forward Anthology*.

Edmund Gwilym Cusick has published poems in *Poetry Wales* and *Poetry Life,* and criticism in the *New Welsh Review*. In 1995 he won first prize in the Avalon Poetry Competition, and was a prize winner in the Aberystwyth Open Poetry Competition. Edmund Cusick teaches Imaginative Writing at Liverpool John Moores University. Previously he was a Lecturer in English Literature at the University of Wales, Lampeter, and also worked as a lexicographer for the *Oxford English Dictionary*.

THE ILLUSTRATOR

Margaret Jones, the Aberystwyth artist, has illustrated many books of Welsh legends including *Y Mabinogi* by Gwyn Thomas (University of Wales Press, 1984; trans. into English, Danish and Gaelic); *Welsh Folk Tales* by Robin Gwyndaf (National Museum of Wales, 1989); *Culhwch ac Olwen* (1988) and *Chwedl Taliesin* (1992) by Gwyn Thomas (U.W.P.; English editions, Lutterworth, Gollancz); and *King Arthur* by Gwyn Thomas and Jenny Nimmo (U.W.P. 1997; English edition, Gollancz). Margaret Jones' work is frequently exhibited. She has also produced poster and card designs, a Calendar of 12 pictures and the *Map of the Mabinogion*.